"What is this plant?" murmured As examined one of the giant stalks.

"This looks like the bamboo the re the wildlife park," said Tess. "I thir

Asha laughed and pointed above Tess's head. "Look! she giggled.

Tess spun around and gazed upwards. A little red panda was lying in the branches of a tree.

"Hello, I'm Shu," she said with a yawn. "Welcome to China."

She stretched and scratched herself behind the ear.

"She doesn't seem surprised to see us," whispered Tess.

Stranded Panda

Written by Adam and Charlotte Guillain

Chapter 1: Sleepy Pandas

One Friday in the summer holidays, Tess's mum took Tess and Asha to the wildlife park.

"Let's go and see the red pandas – they're so cute!" said Tess.

"Yes!" said Asha, rushing after Tess.

At first, they couldn't see a glimpse of the red pandas, then Asha whispered, "Look, they're sleeping in that tree."

"It says here that red pandas live in China, like giant pandas," said Tess.

"And they both enjoy eating bamboo," read Asha.

As they watched the sleepy creatures, the sun peeped out from behind a cloud, dazzling the friends. The next moment, they felt their feet rise up in the air!

"Do you think we're going to China?" asked Tess as they were whirled away.

"Who knows – maybe!" cried Asha.

When they stopped, Asha and Tess stared at the forest around them. Huge, straight plant stalks grew high among the trees and the forest glowed green in the sunlight shining down.

"Have you ever seen humans before?" asked Asha.

Shu sighed. "A year ago I had never seen a human," she told them, "but now things have changed."

"What do you mean?" asked Tess with a frown.

"Follow me and I'll show you," said Shu.

Chapter 2: The Forest

Shu clambered down to the forest floor and led Tess and Asha through the trees. They walked in silence, hearing only the crack of twigs under their feet and birds singing. Then Asha heard a new sound.

"What's that noise?" she asked, glancing about.

"That's what I wanted to show you," whispered Shu.

They moved forward to a gap in the trees, and Tess and Asha gasped. Ahead of them was a large area of earth, dotted with ragged tree stumps and in the distance a truck loaded with logs was trundling away.

"People have been cutting down the forest," sighed Shu.

"But there's still some left for you, isn't there?" said Asha.

Shu shook her head. "It's not enough. When trees are chopped down, it's hard for us to find enough food or other red pandas, because they leave to search for food. We can get stuck on our own."

Asha shuddered as she gazed at the ruined forest.

"I'm going back to sleep," sighed Shu, heading back into the forest. "I'm not normally awake during the day." She waved to them as she climbed up a tree and then disappeared.

"Let's explore a bit more," said Tess.

They made their way back into the dense forest. Soon the sound of trucks and diggers had disappeared and they followed a stream through the trees.

"Wouldn't it be amazing to see a giant panda too?" said Asha, glancing around hopefully.

"They're very rare," said Tess, "but let's keep looking."

A loud roaring noise made the friends suddenly stop.

"I hope that's not a tiger," whispered Asha, her eyes wide with fear. "Are there tigers in China?"

Tess nodded and glanced around as all grew quiet again. They jumped as an even louder roar burst through the silence.

They crept forwards, looking around for any sign of danger. The green shadows of the forest fell away and the girls found themselves standing on the edge of a muddy track. A huge truck was roaring and rumbling into the distance.

At the edge of the track, a rocky slope ran down to the right.

"There's something down there," said Asha. "Look! It's black and white."

Tess stepped along slowly and peered over the edge.

"It's a giant panda!" she cried. "He's stuck!"

Chapter 3: Stuck!

Tess and Asha stared down at the terrified face below them.

"Help me," pleaded the panda. "I was just wandering through the forest when the trees disappeared and I slid down here."

Asha and Tess carefully scrambled down the slope until they were alongside the panda.

"I'm Ming," he said when they had reached him. "Please help me, I'm frightened."

"Watch me climb and copy me," Asha showed Ming where to put his paws and climb upwards.

Ming started to follow Asha, but as his paws gripped the slope, he slid back down – he was too heavy. Stones and soil showered down below him.

"Look out!" shouted Tess, who was waiting below.

"Sorry," whimpered Ming. "I think I'm stuck here forever."

Asha climbed back down and stroked Ming's head.

"What are we going to do?" Asha whispered to Tess.

Tess looked up and shook her head. It would be impossible for Ming to climb up. Then she looked down at the foot of the slope, where the edge of the forest lay.

"I've got an idea," she said with a smile.

Chapter 4: Let's Slide

Tess gently tapped Ming on the shoulder and he hid his face and trembled.

"Don't be scared, I've got an idea," said Tess softly.

Slowly, Ming turned and looked at Tess as Asha stroked his ears.

"We could slide down the slope!" said Tess, grinning.

Ming quickly shook his head, but Tess squeezed his shoulder.

"Watch this," she said, before turning around and leaning back into the slope. Little by little, Tess let her feet slip down until she had slid all the way down to the bottom.

"You go next, Ming!" Tess called.

Ming shuddered and looked away.

"You can do it!" urged Asha, but he shook his head again.

"You go next," he wailed. "I'm not – it's too terrifying."

Asha hesitated but she knew Ming wasn't going to budge.

"Okay," she said, and started sliding down the slope.

When Asha got to the bottom, she turned to look up at Ming.

"Come on, Ming," she shouted. "It's easy!"

But Ming clung on to the bush with his eyes closed and didn't move a muscle.

"He's too scared," said Tess. "What are we going to do?"

Chapter 5: Hungry

The girls gazed up at the stranded panda and Tess felt a sinking feeling in her stomach.

"We can't climb all the way back up now," she said. "How are we going to help him?"

"He must be getting tired and hungry," sighed Asha.

Asha frowned as she watched Tess stride into the forest.

"Asha, can you come and help?" asked Tess as she stood next to a large bamboo stalk.

Asha helped Tess snap the stalk off at the bottom.

"Giant pandas are always hungry," Tess said, her eyes twinkling.

They carried the huge bamboo stalk back to the bottom of the slope and held it up towards Ming.

At first, nothing happened. Then Ming raised his head, hesitated, and sniffed.

"He can smell it," whispered Asha.

Ming glanced down and reached out one paw for the bamboo.

"Come on, Ming!" coaxed Tess, gently waving the bamboo.

Ming let go of the bush and slid a few centimetres down
the slope.

"You're nearly there!" called Asha. Ming gave a tiny smile and
slid a little more … and a little more …

"You did it!" cried Tess as Ming reached the bottom.

He munched the bamboo. "Thank you," he said as a beam of bright sunlight shone through the forest trees.

Asha felt her feet lift up. "We're going home," she said.

"Goodbye!" called Tess as they were carried back to the wildlife park.

Tess held out her hand. "Look – a piece of bamboo," she said.

Mrs Knight had asked her class to collect six things over the holidays.

"This says there are organisations that protect wild pandas," read Asha.

"Let's look on the Internet when we get home," Tess decided. "Maybe we can do something to help?"

Stranded Panda

What other things will the Comet Street Kids collect
for their holiday challenge? Read the other books
in this band to find out!

Stranded Panda

A Midsummer Night's Disaster

The Missing Cat

Moonquake

Brilliant Braille

Stop Shouting!

Talk about the story

Answer the questions:

1 What is the name of the country where red pandas live?

2 What do both types of panda like to eat?

3 Why did Shu say that 'things have changed'? (page 7)

4 What does the word 'ragged' mean? (page 9)

5 What was the name of the giant panda?

6 Why was Ming scared?

7 Can you describe in your own words what Tess's first idea was to help Ming? Did it work? What happened next?

8 Do you know of any other animals that are endangered? What can we do to help them?

Can you retell the story in your own words?